ISBN 0-85079-139-1

D1079803

The GAMBOLS

BOOK Nº 33

by Dobs + Barry Appleby

£1·35

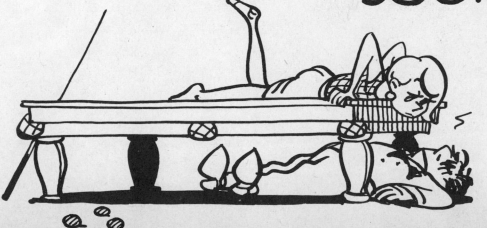

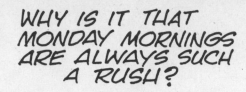

2599

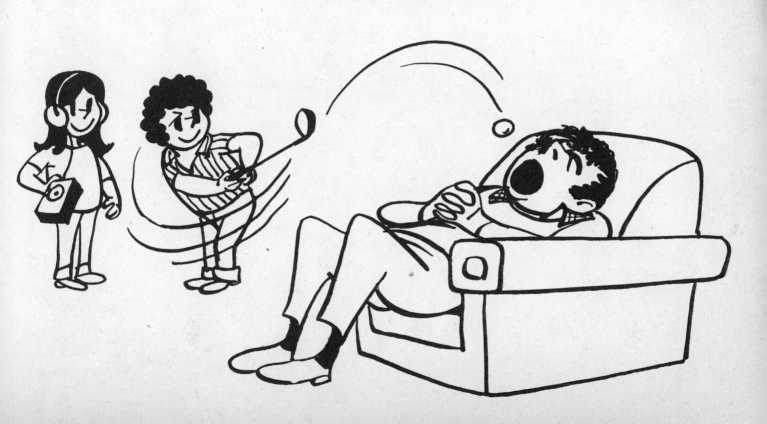

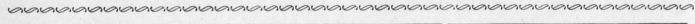

SOMEBODY RECENTLY SAID
THAT MORE BUSINESS IS DONE
ON THE GOLF COURSE THAN
IN THE OFFICE

DARLING I LOVE YOU FOR NOT SAYING "I TOLD YOU SO"

©1985 Dobs + Barry Appleby

2622

I'VE INVENTED A NEW SUPER FAST WEEDKILLER

IT'LL MAKE OUR FORTUNE —ALL YOU HAVE TO DO IS TO SPRAY THE WEEDS

AND IT BURNS UP EVERY THING IT TOUCHES

©1985 Dobs + Barry Appleby

2619

WELL, IT'S TURNED OUT TO BE A **BEAUTIFUL** DAY

18-3

HULLO

CAN I SPEAK TO GAYE?

JUST A MINUTE

WHO IS IT?

GAYE WANTS TO KNOW WHO IT IS BEFORE SHE COMMITS HERSELF

2612

AUGH!

HULLO—WHAT'S A NICE GIRL LIKE YOU DOING IN A PLACE LIKE THIS

17-4

BY THE WAY— I'LL BE LATE HOME TO·NIGHT

OH?

I HAVE TO TAKE AN IMPORTANT CLIENT OUT TO DINNER

OH? WHAT'S HIS NAME?

FLOSI GLAMOORE

2611

(SLAM)

GEORGE DEAR—PROMISE YOU WON'T LAUGH....

© 1983 Dobs + Barry Appleby

2610

DON'T BE SUCH A BABY GEORGE

I'LL SOON GET THIS GREAT BIG SPLINTER OUT

NEEDLES

.... IF I CAN SEE IT

NEEDLES

© 1983 Dobs + Barry Appleby

2609

GEORGE
LOVES A
PICNIC
BUT
GAYE'S
NOT SO
SURE

25-9

WE'LL HAVE TO BE IN BETTER TRAINING THAN THIS...

...IF WE'RE GOING TO PAINT BOTH BEDROOMS AND THE BATHROOM

HOW MUCH PAINT DO YOU THINK WE SHALL NEED?

PAINTS

SPECIAL OFFER

OH-ABOUT TWO LITRES

AND HOW MANY LITRES OF BEER?

EEK!

OH FOR HEAVEN'S SAKE— STOP MOANING

I **TOLD** YOU THAT IT WOULDN'T BE EASY TO RE·TILE THE ROOF. OURSELVES

2782

EEK!

MY NAILS!

I'D LIKE AN APPOINTMENT FOR A FACIAL, SHAMPOO AND SET AND A MANICURE

IT WOULD HAVE BEEN CHEAPER **NOT** TO HAVE DONE IT OURSELVES

© 1983 Dobs + Barry Appleby

2608

THE FOLLOWING PAGES CONTAIN SOME OF THE LARGER GAMBOLS CARTOONS WHICH YOU MAY NOT HAVE SEEN BEFORE IN THIS COUNTRY

858

859

860

854

847

874

875

877

879

867

865

842

871

872

WELL GEORGE — **YOU** OFFERED TO DO THE HOUSEWORK WHILE I WAS SHOPPING

AND I WARNED YOU THAT IT WOULDN'T BE EASY

851

·837

WE'VE BEEN BROUGHT UP TO BELIEVE THAT POLITENESS PAYS...BUT NOT ALWAYS THESE DAYS

HOW MANY TIMES HAVE *YOU* BEEN CAUGHT LIKE THIS — WITH THE BILL?

© 1983 Dobs + Barry Appleby

2722

THE TROUBLE WITH CHILDREN THESE DAYS IS THAT THEY KNOW SO MUCH MORE ABOUT COMPUTERS —ESPECIALLY COMPUTER GAMES— THAN WE DO

2684

2696

WHAT IS IT ABOUT SPIDERS THAT FRIGHTENS SOME PEOPLE WHO ARE NORMALLY BRAVE ENOUGH TO FACE A MAD DOG OR A FEROCIOUS LION?

I ALWAYS MAKE A RESOLUTION TO READ THE INSTRUCTIONS CAREFULLY AND FIRST — BUT I NEVER DO

HALF AN HOUR LATER

ANOTHER HALF HOUR

WHAT DO YOU MEAN— YOU FORGOT TO GO TO THE BANK?

© 1983 Dobs + Barry Appleby

2698

THEY'RE ABSOLUTELY THE LATEST AND **VERY** FASHIONABLE

© 1984 Dobs + Barry Appleby

DON'T **YOU** FIND THEM EVEN THE **TINIEST** BIT SEXY?

WELL..ER... SURE YOU HAVEN'T GOT THEM ON UPSIDE DOWN OR SOMETHING?

¼

GEORGE'S FANCY DRESS COSTUME IS A BIT GRUESOME ISN'T IT?

WELL—FANCY DRESS ISN'T THE MAIN PURPOSE

IT'S REALLY INTENDED TO HELP HIM KEEP HIS RESOLUTION NOT TO DRINK AND DRIVE

©1984 Dobs + Barry Appleby

2818

IT'S THOSE YOUNG CAROL SINGERS YOU TURNED AWAY EARLIER

WELL, I'LL TURN THEM AWAY **AGAIN**

©1984 Dobs + Barry Appleby

2812

AND THIS IS THE END OF YET
ANOTHER GAMBOLS ANNUAL—
'BYE FOR NOW—SEE YOU IN
THE MORNING

© 1984 Dobs + Barry Appleby

Published by Express Newspapers Limited, Fleet Street, London, EC4P 4JT, and printed by Purnell and Sons (Book Production) Ltd., Paulton, Bristol.